BOOK THREE

A DOZEN A DAY

Pre-Practice
Technical Exercises
FOR THE PIANO

by

Edna-Mae Burnam

THE WILLIS MUSIC COMPANY

To my daughter " Pat "

A DOZEN A DAY

Many people do physical exercises every morning before they go to work.

Likewise—we should all give our fingers exercises every day BEFORE we begin our practising.

The purpose of this book is to help develop strong hands and flexible fingers, and a firm touch.

The finger exercises may be played slowly and softly at first; then gradually faster and louder.

The chord exercises may be played *mp*, *mf*, and *f*, for variation, and at a moderate rate of speed.

Do not try to learn the entire first dozen exercises the first week you study this book! Just learn two or three exercises and do them each day *before* practising. When these are mastered, add another, then another, and keep adding until the twelve can be played perfectly.

When the first dozen—Group I—have been mastered and perfected—Group II may be introduced in the same manner.

When the entire book is finished, any of the groups may be transposed to different keys. In fact, this should be encouraged.

EDNA-MAE BURNAM

CONTENTS

To my daughter "Pat"

Group I
1. Wake up and Stretch

2. Brushing Teeth

accent

3. Going Down Stairs

4. Chinning Yourself

Set fingers silent.
Hold down throughout exercise.

Play entire exercise with thumbs

5. Walking

6. Running

or 2 d.

6 = 6 ♪s in a bar
8

7. Jumping

8. Backward Bend

9. Flinging Arms Out and Back

10. Cartwheels

11. The Push-Up

12. Fit as a Fiddle and Ready To Go

Group II

1. Deep Breathing

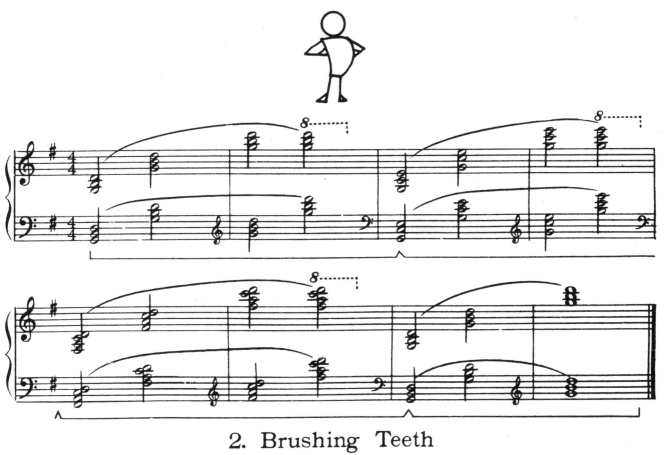

2. Brushing Teeth

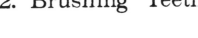

3. The Broad Jump

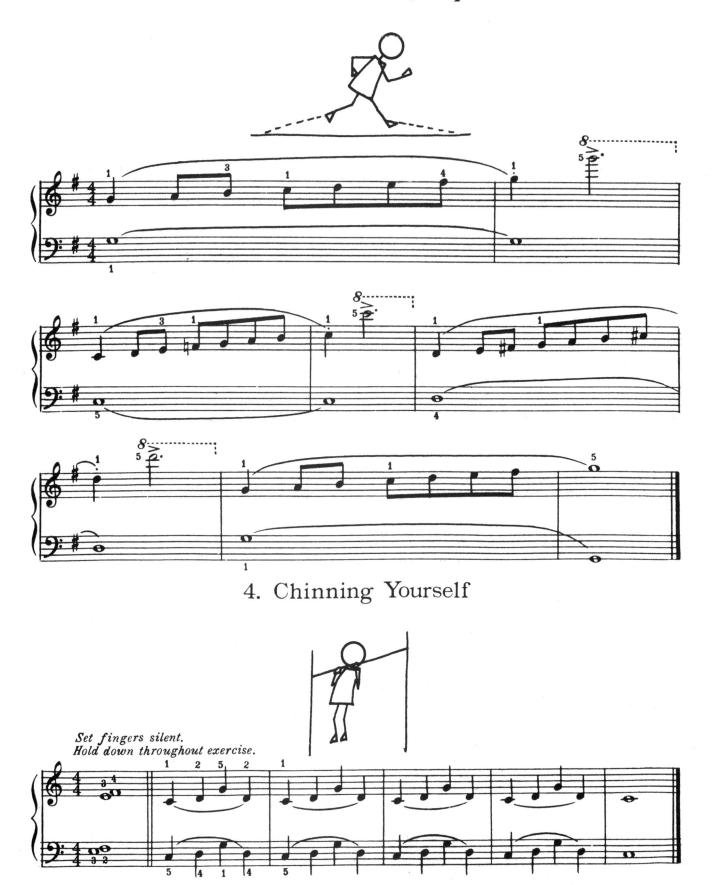

4. Chinning Yourself

Set fingers silent.
Hold down throughout exercise.

5. Climbing (in place)

6. The Splits

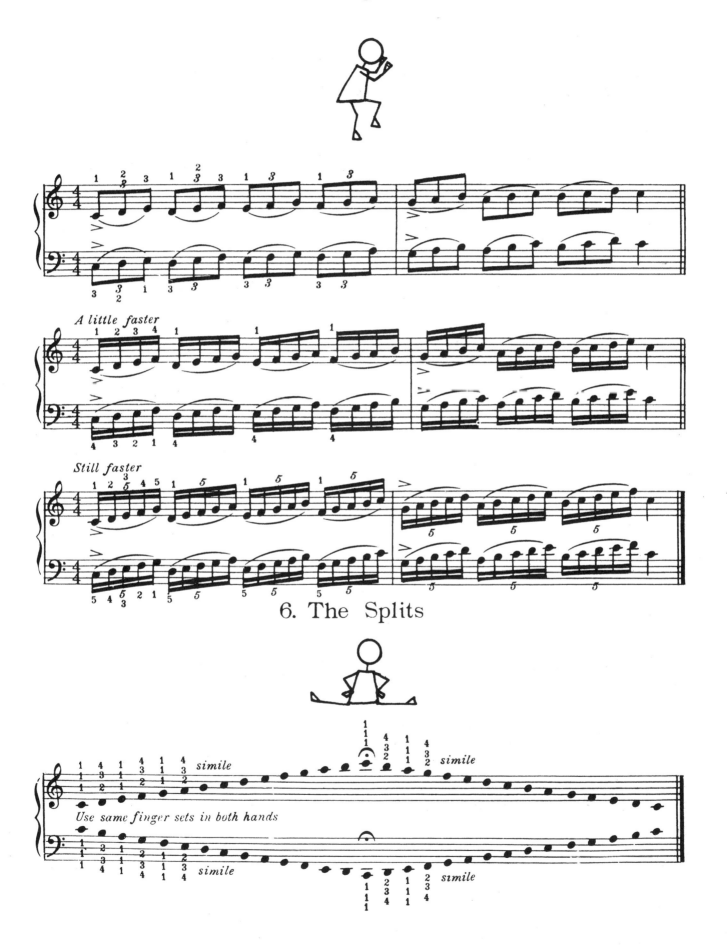

7. O-Leary

One, two, three O - Lear - y
Four, five, six O - Lear - y

Seven, eight, nine O - Lear - y
Ten, eleven, twelve O - Lear - y.
One O - Lear - y two O - Lear - y

three O - Lear - y four.
I would like to do O - Lear - y
for for - ev - er - more.

8. Leap Frog

9. Jump The River

10. Whirling

14

11. Going Up Stairs

12. Fit as a Fiddle and Ready To Go

Group III
1. Wake Up and Stretch

2. Deep Breathing

3. Jumping Feet Apart and Flinging Arms Out

4. Crossing Leg Over (lying down)

5. Chinning Yourself

18

6. Tip-toe Running (in place)

7. Kicking Right Leg

8. Kicking Left Leg

9. Jumping Like A Frog (both feet at once)

20

10. Running

11. Cartwheels

12. Fit as a Fiddle and Ready To Go

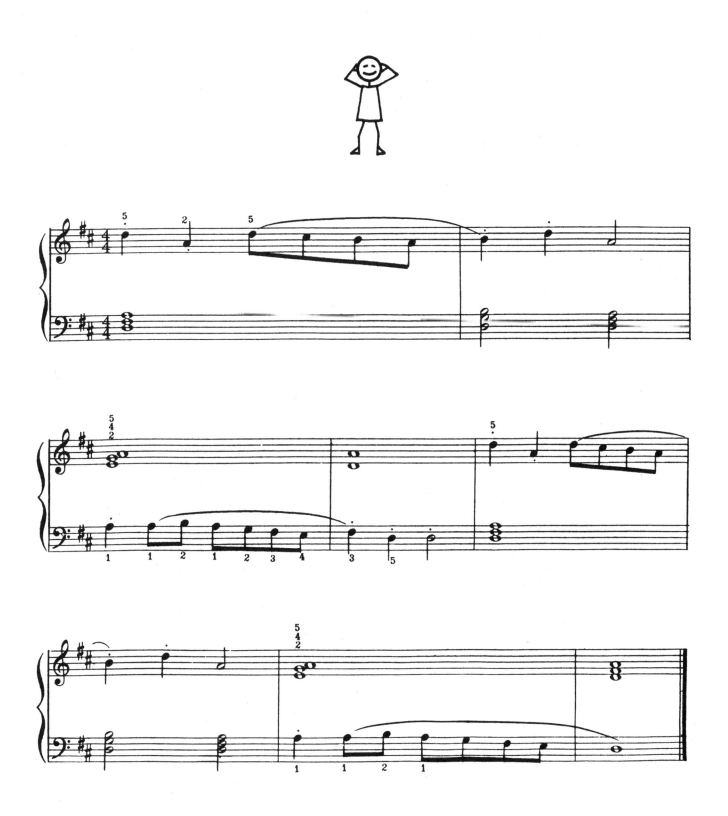

Group IV

1. Deep Breathing

2. Cartwheels

3. Walking On Stilts

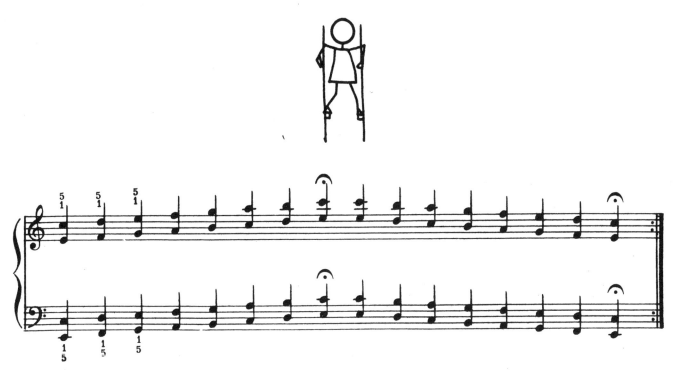

4. Walking a Tightrope

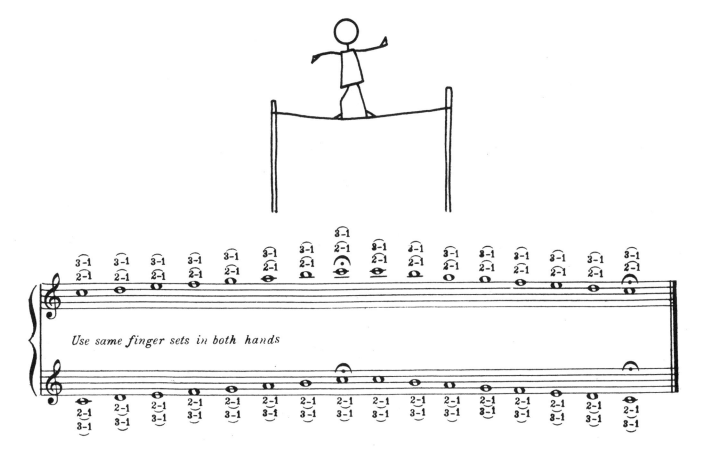

Use same finger sets in both hands

5. Chinning Yourself

6. Going Up and Down a Rope

7. Skipping

8. Running

9. Turning Right Leg Around In a Circle

10. Turning Left Leg Around In a Circle

11. Hanging By Your Knees

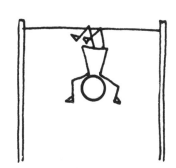

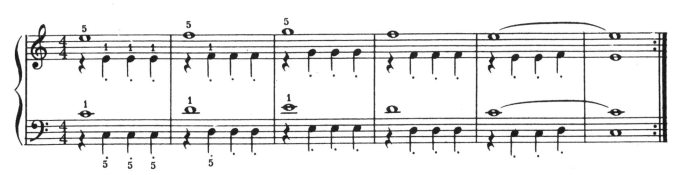

12. Fit as a Fiddle and Ready To Go

Group V

1. Deep Breathing

2. Sliding Down A Pole (a little bit at a time)

5. Bicycle Exercise

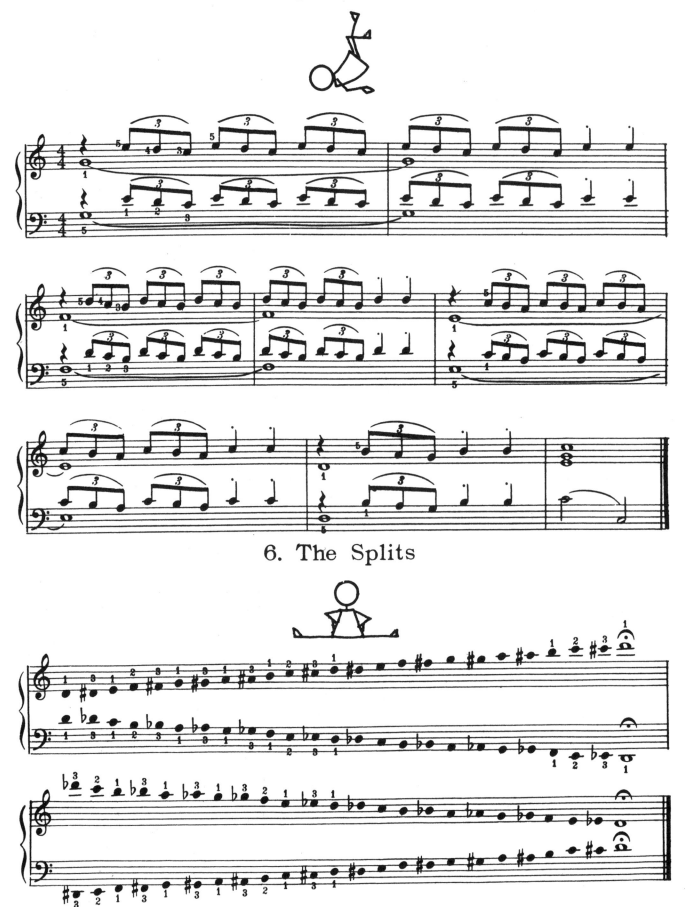

6. The Splits

7. Up and Down the Stairs

8. Running Down A Hill

9. Deep Knee Bend

10. Leap Frog

11. Climbing

12. Fit as a Fiddle and Ready To Go

Track Listing

Each track is split – hear both piano and accompaniment if
the balance is centred, the accompaniment only if the balance
control is to the left, and the piano only if it is to the right!